A Journey of Faith
Legg-Calvé-Perthes

Bone of His Bone, Flesh of His Flesh

SHRINER'S
HOSPITAL

by Karen Jordan & Channy Jordan
Illustrated by Channy Jordan & Karen Jordan

Library of Congress Control Number: 2017952739

ISBN:
978-1-63308-335-6 (hardback)
978-1-63308-282-3 (paperback)
978-1-63308-283-0 (ebook)

Interior Design by *R'tor John D. Maghuyop*
Illustrated by *Channy Jordan & Karen Jordan*

CHALFANT ECKERT
PUBLISHING

1028 S Bishop Avenue, Dept. 178
Rolla, MO 65401

Printed in United States of America

A Journey of Faith Through
Legg-Calvé-Perthes Disease

Bone of His Bone, Flesh of His Flesh

by Karen Jordan & Channy Jordan

Illustrated by Channy Jordan & Karen Jordan

CHALFANT ECKERT
PUBLISHING

artwork by Jonathan

Hi! My name is Jonathan. My family and friends call me Channy.

When I was eight years old, I walked with a limp.
I didn't know I limped and I never complained
of any pain.

My dad asked my mom to take me to our
chiropractor, Dr. Rob. He did some tests and told
my mom that maybe I had a broken bone
in my pelvis area.

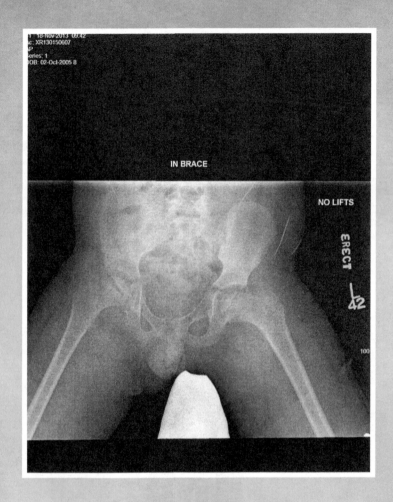

He sent us for x-rays, and then he called my mom. He asked, "Good news or bad news first?" We chose to hear the good news first!

"Good news is that time can heal this. Bad news is that Jonathan has Legg-Calvé-Perthes Disease."

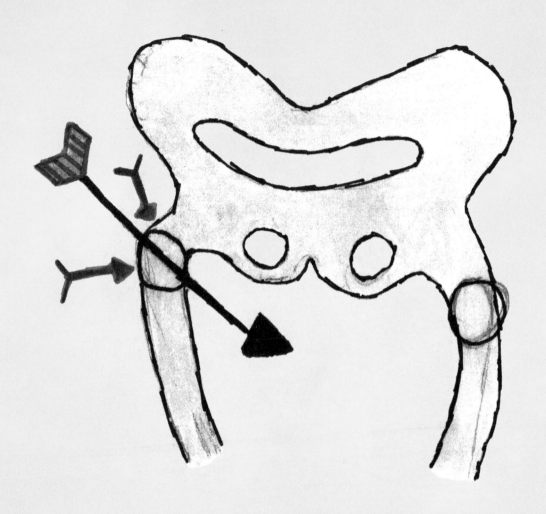

Legg-Calvé-Perthes Disease is a problem with the femoral ball, where the leg attaches to the hip. Somehow the blood supply becomes cut off, and the head of the femur dies.

We were sent to a specialist in St. Louis, Missouri. She was very nice, and she helped us understand that my leg needed time to heal.

John 12:24 "Listen carefully: Unless a grain of wheat
is buried in the ground, dead to the world,
it is never any more than a grain of wheat.
But if it is buried, it sprouts and reproduces
itself many times over."

1 Corinthians 15:36 "What a foolish question!
When you put a seed into the ground,
it doesn't grow into a plant unless it dies first."

For Legg-Calvé-Perthes Disease to heal, the
femoral ball has to die all the way before it can
come back to life. During the whole process,
the doctors worked to protect my hip.

My family was devastated. I am the youngest of
nine children, and I love to play ball - any kind of
ball. Some would call me a child prodigy. My dream
in life is to become a pro baseball player
and play for the St. Louis Cardinals.

I would not be able to run or play sports until my leg healed. My doctor said she didn't know how long that would take.

When my parents began to share about my disease, a good friend of theirs offered to send us to Shriners Hospital.

My new doctor was not as smiley and kind
as the first one, but she cared about me.
She told us I would be fitted for A-frames and
I would have to be in a wheelchair or on
crutches most of the time.

The first night I tried to sleep in my
A-frames I cried until I sobbed and my mom
and dad said I could take them off.

I had to have special socks and stockings
to be able to wear my frames. I went to
Shriners once every few months for x-rays,
exams and anything I needed.

When I found out I would have to be in a
wheelchair, I wanted to be homeschooled.
I thought all the kids would make fun of me
and they would not help me.

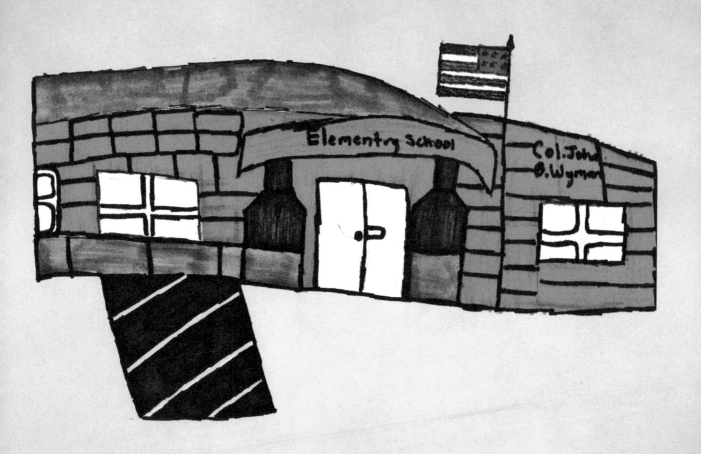

The first day I went to school in my wheelchair and frames I was nervous. I feared everyone would make fun of me. That was not the case! Everyone was surprised by my condition, but no one has ever ridiculed me.

My school turned out to be an awesome blessing!
Not only were my classmates nice and became
my helpers wherever I went, the school had an
elevator. Everybody did everything they
could to help me.

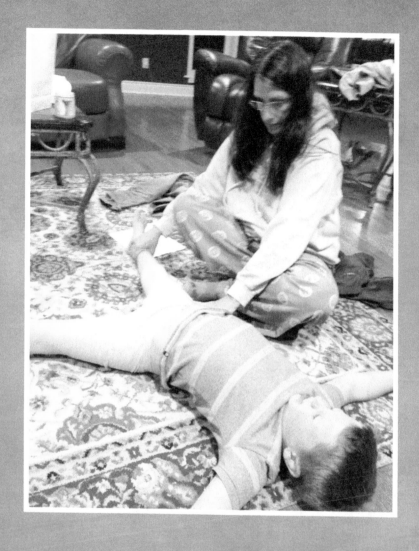

My mom became my physical therapist.
She helped me to stay limber and have a good
range of motion. We would sit on the floor in the
morning, and she would stretch my legs.

Soon we were used to my being restricted from playing and running. My siblings were so very sad for me. My sister decided to find someone who had overcome Legg-Calvé-Perthes Disease to inspire me.

She found a college baseball player who had recovered from Legg-Calvé-Perthes Disease and contacted him. He agreed to talk with me and encouraged my family and me that we would get through this. I got to meet him and sit in his college dugout during a game.

I also beg007an hyperbaric oxygen chamber
treatments at my chiropractor's office.
My grandparents had great healing experiences
with this therapy and they paid for me
to have some treatments.

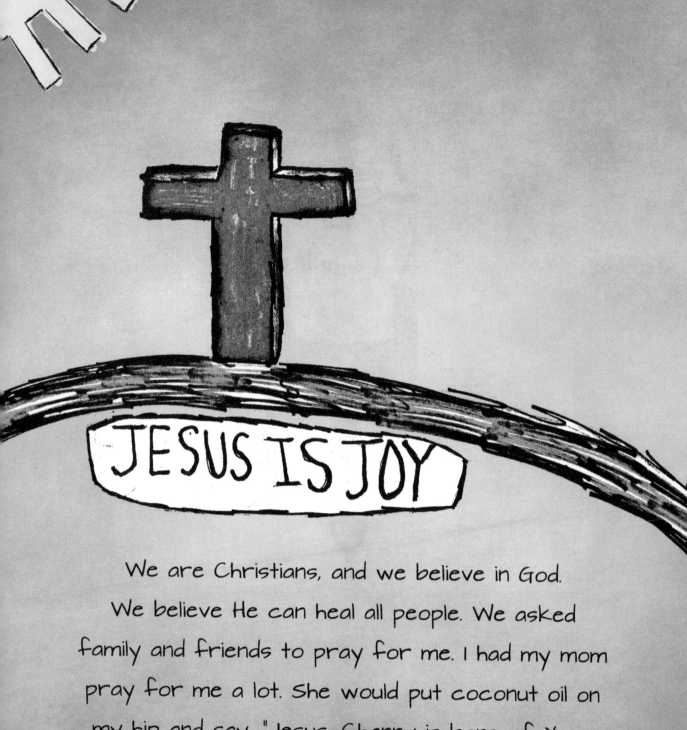

JESUS IS JOY

We are Christians, and we believe in God.
We believe He can heal all people. We asked
family and friends to pray for me. I had my mom
pray for me a lot. She would put coconut oil on
my hip and say, "Jesus, Channy is bone of Your
bone and flesh of Your flesh. Thank You
for Channy's healing."

Time went on, and my progress was slow.
A year after becoming a patient at Shriners
Hospital, I had to change doctors -- again. My
new doctor seemed concerned with my lack of
change and told us that I might need surgery.

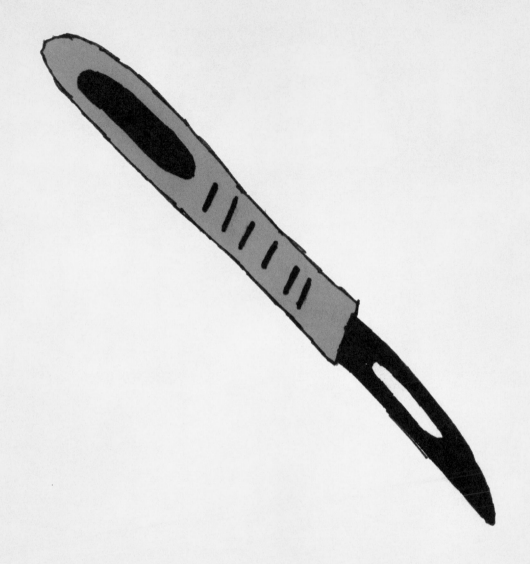

My doctor decided to perform a surgery called "adductor percutaneous tendon lengthening." From x-rays and an MRI, he thought I had a deep indention on the femoral ball, and I needed my hip to be opened up and have major work done to it.

At nine and a half years old I had my surgery.
I was really scared. We stayed in St. Louis the
night before and went to Shriners early the next
morning. We had lots of people praying
for my doctor and me.

When I was in surgery, the doctor called my
mom and dad into the prep room. They were not
sure what he was going to tell them. He said,
"GOOD NEWS!! Jonathan does not need what I
thought. This is a relatively simple surgery,
and we will be done quickly."

My mom said, "Praise the Lord! Channy
is bone of His bone and flesh of His flesh!"

I had a hard time waking up from surgery.
I was numb from the waist down, and I was
in leg casts. I hated it.

My mom and I slept in the downstairs room of our house for six weeks. She took great care of me. Even though it was inconvenient, we both loved the time we spent together.

My third-grade teacher came to my house twice
a week to tutor me through the end of school.
She was an amazing teacher who believed
in God with me for my healing.

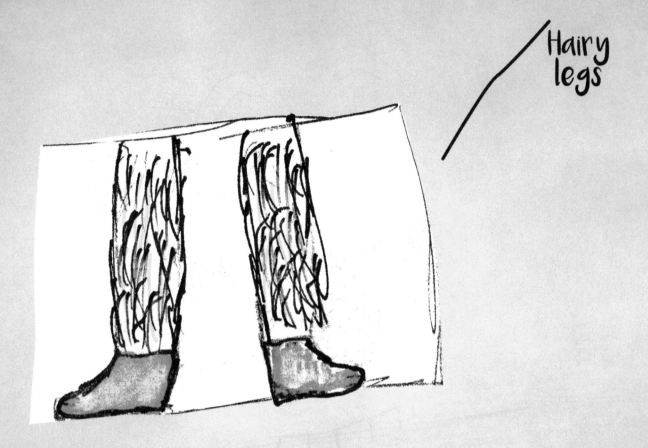

Hairy legs

After about six weeks my casts were removed. I was nervous to have them cut off. I was used to them, and I didn't want any more pain. Fortunately, it didn't hurt for them to be cut off. My legs just looked funny and hairy!

It took me a while to try my legs.
Once I started putting a little weight on them,
I wasn't scared anymore.

We got through that summer - another summer
I did not get to play baseball. I was asked to be a
bat boy and sit on the bench, but I said, "NO!" I felt
in my heart that someday I would play again!

I started fourth grade, and it was the same old routine. I had to be in my A-frames in my wheelchair at school, and I could use my crutches at home.

Jonathan Jordan
John Light
Vicki Smith
Abraham McDaniel
Ivy Lane
Melissa Davis
Monica Vickery
Michael Watson

All this time we prayed, believing that my bones were Jesus' bones and my flesh was His flesh. When I would go to church, I would look for my name on the prayer lists. I liked knowing many people were praying for me.

After two years and four months,
we went to an appointment and my doctor said
my x-rays showed bone!! He seemed surprised.
He said my femoral ball was bone and it was
round, two things we had been waiting to hear
for a long time!

He said no more A-frames. No more wheelchair.
No more crutches (except for long distances).
No more limping! My mom asked if I could play
ball and the doctor said, "Whoa! Slow down!
Not yet." He said my bone and muscle
needed to strengthen.

The physical therapist gave us exercises to do at home to strengthen my leg. What a journey this has been! I asked my mom if she would write a book. This is it! This is my story.

I thank God that He provided my healing through Jesus. I thank God for prayers, family, friends, and doctors.

I can't wait to play baseball and run as fast as
my nephews, Chayton and Chancen.

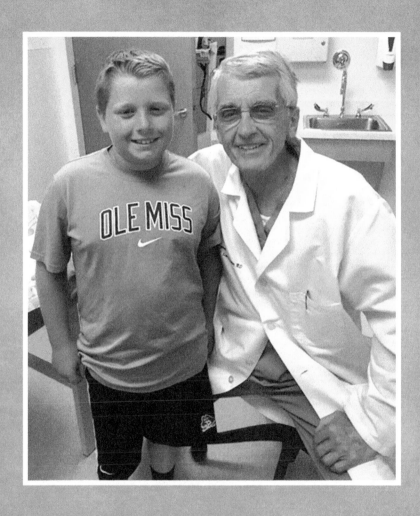

I will always remember I am bone of His bone
and flesh of His flesh.

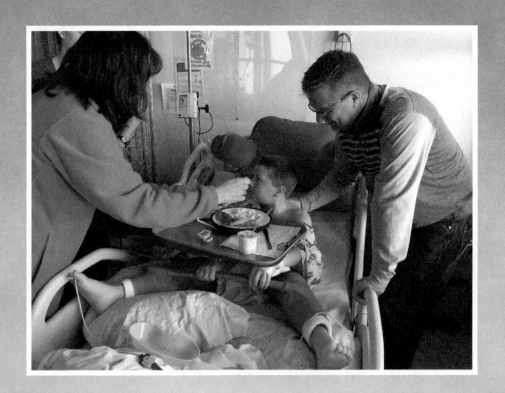

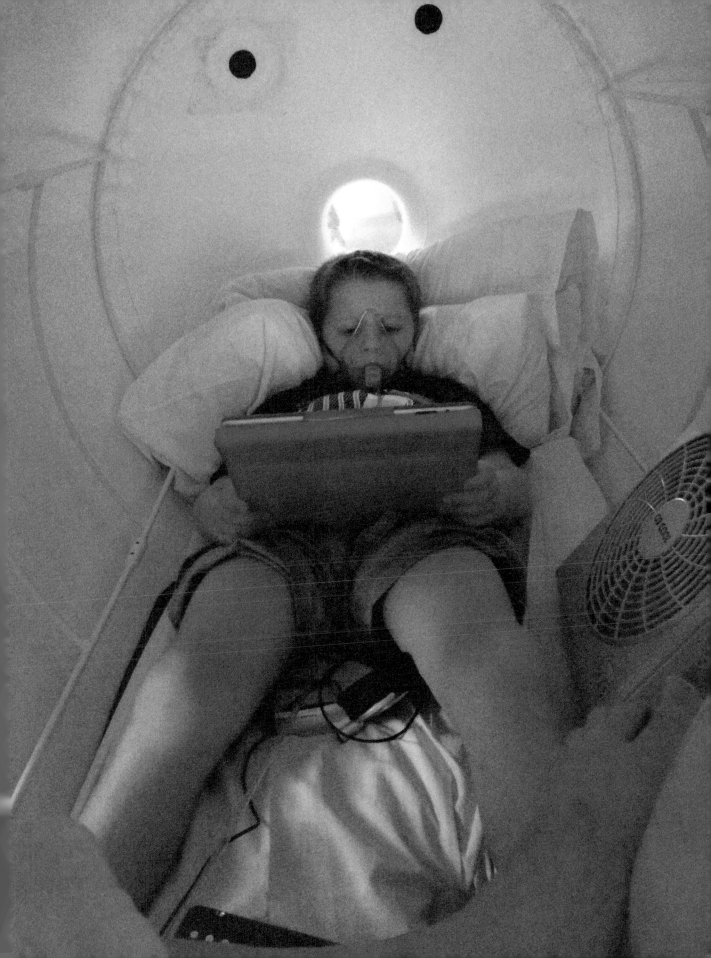

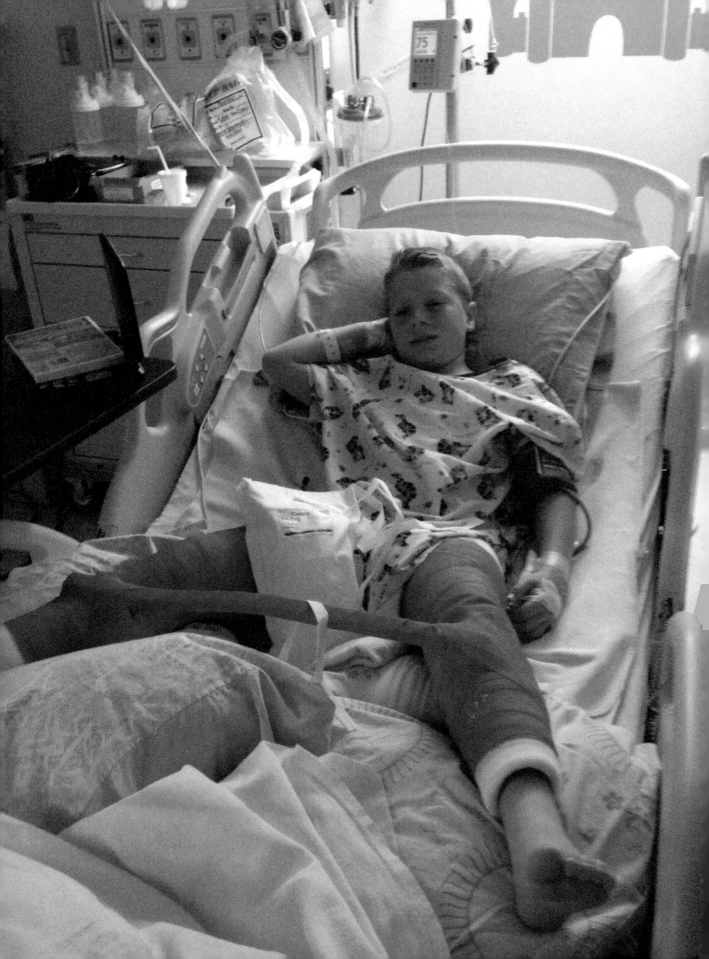

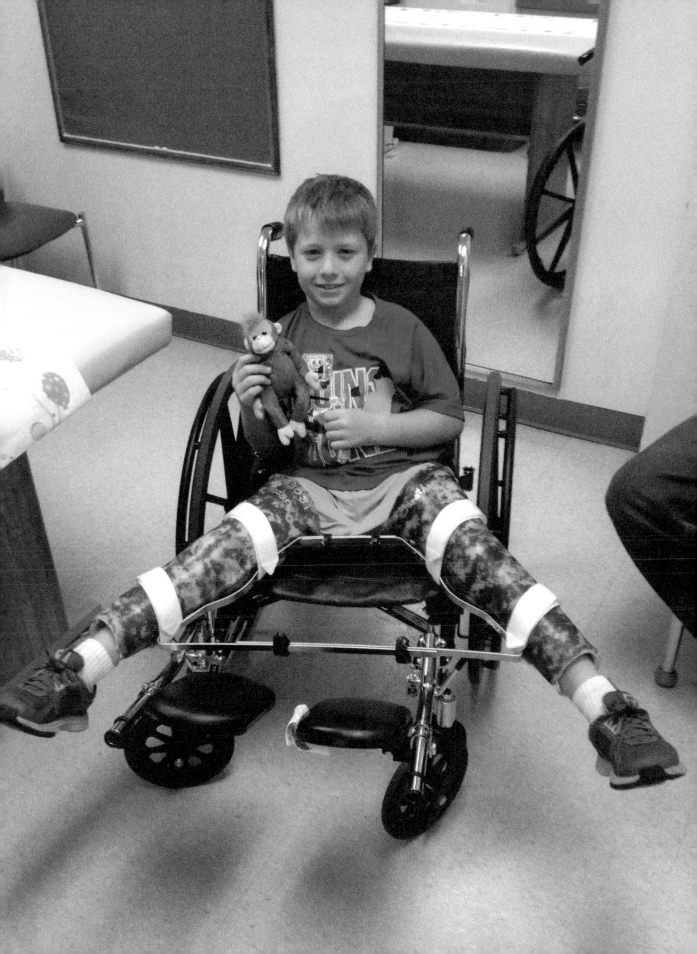

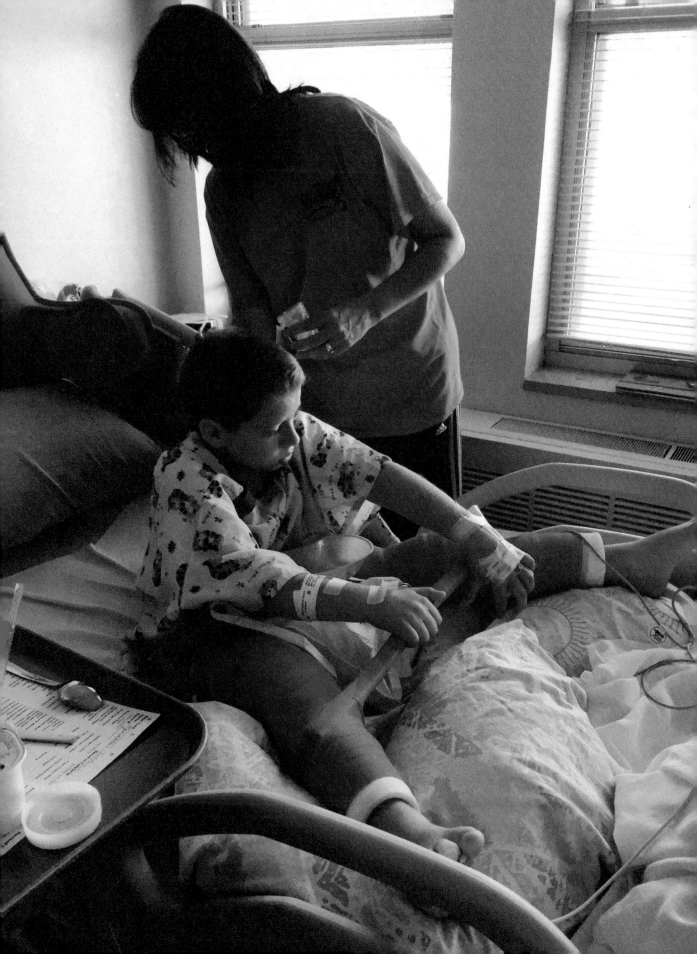

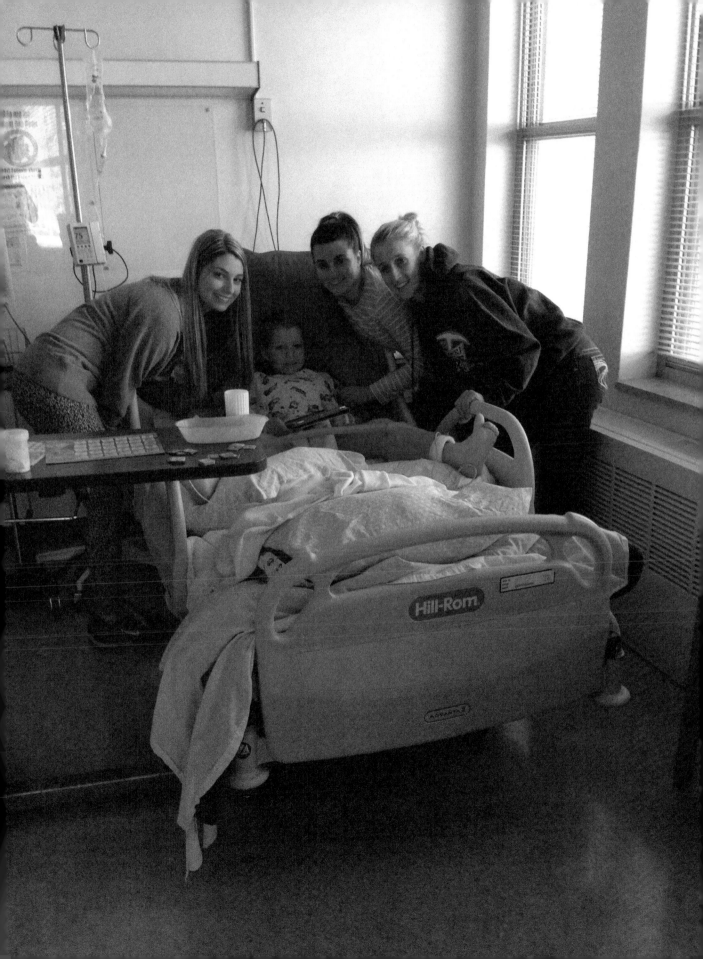

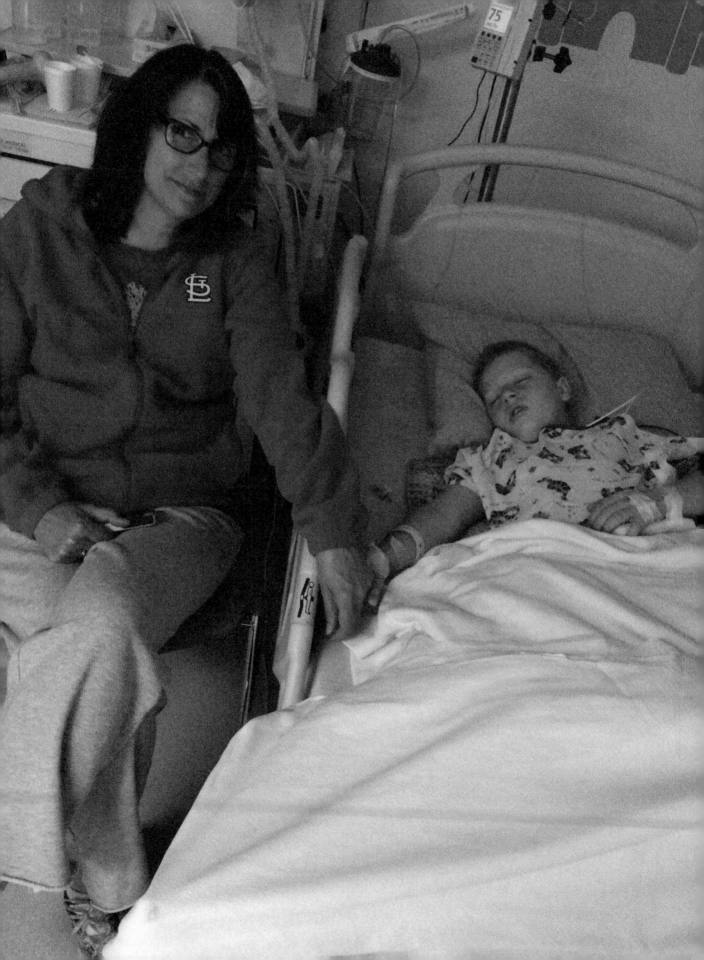

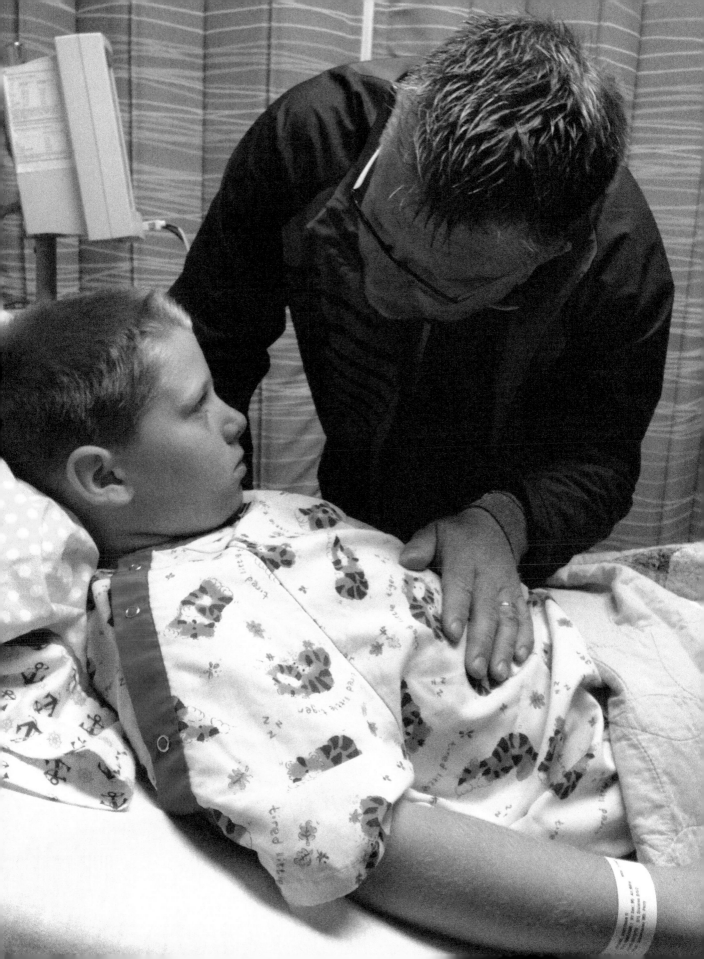

CPSIA information can be obtained
at www.ICGtesting.com
Printed in the USA
BVOW07s1617091117

499908BV00004B/95/P